ratner

People loved listening to the stories Jesus told.

One day Jesus told them about a very rich farmer who had two sons. The elder son worked all day and every day on his father's farm.

But the younger son did not like hard work. Instead he asked his father for his share of the money that would have come to him when his father died.

His father was sad, but he divided up his land between the two sons. The younger son sold his share and left home with all the money.

He used his money to have some great parties... and to buy fine clothes... and he gave lots of it to his new friends. As long as he was rich, he was very popular.

But when the money ran out, so did his friends. Before very long the younger brother had nothing.

To make matters worse there was a great famine in the country. No one had enough to eat. The son grew more and more hungry.

He ended up in rags, and the only job he could get was to look after a load of smelly pigs! He was so hungry he felt like fighting the pigs for their food!

The young man was very sad. He thought the only thing left for him to do was to go back home to his father, and say he was very, very, very sorry, and ask for a job on the farm. He started the long, long trudge home.

The Loving Father

Pull out the stickers and these middle pages.
Then read what to do next from the back page.

Now
use your
stickers!

This is what to do:

1. **Read the story right through so you know what happens.**
2. **Peel off each sticker carefully.**
3. **Use each sticker to complete the picture on the pages you have pulled out.**

More sticker books to collect!

There are 48 stories in this series, all with stickers. Collect all the stories and stick the completed middle pages round your bedroom wall.

Meanwhile his father had spent every day and night waiting for his son to return. So when he spotted his son staggering over the hill, he was thrilled!

The old man dashed down to meet his long lost son. He was so excited he did a couple of somersaults!

His son got ready to say how sorry he was for running away and wasting all his father's money. But before he could get the words out, his father hugged and kissed him. He found him some of the finest clothes in the country and he even gave him a gold ring to wear.

The young man could not believe it was happening. "I'm really sorry!" he said to his father. "I don't deserve to be forgiven like this."

"I can forgive so much because I love you so much," said his father, grinning. He then arranged for the biggest and best party there had ever been in the land.

The elder brother was a bit grumpy about all this. He thought he should have had a big party too. After all, he had worked very hard indeed. He had never given his father any trouble at all.

"But..." said his father, "this is my son who was lost, and now he is found! I thought he was dead, but instead he's alive! Surely you can't blame me for having a party, can you?"

Jesus had finished his story. He smiled at all the people who had been listening.

"That story gives you a good idea of what God is like," said Jesus. "He just can't wait for his children to come back to him to say sorry for the bad or silly things they have done. That's just the sort of 'dad' God is."